KPA

ANIMAL CAMOUFLAGE

Animal Camouflage

by Adolf Portmann

ANN ARBOR

THE UNIVERSITY OF MICHIGAN PRESS

Contents

INTRODUCTION

The rugged outline of a mountain peak looks like a
human face; the markings on a moth show a skull and
crossbones. Mere coincidences we say, and dismiss the
matter as another freak of nature. But when we come
across an animal that looks like a leaf or a twig, we begin
to wonder. This likeness must be more than chance—it
must play an important part in the animal's survival.
This brings us straight to the crux of our problem: the
function of outward appearances.

We have all seen insects that are the color of bark and
brooding pheasant hens whose feathers seem like the
fleeting shadows of their nesting ground. We may have
chanced upon a moth whose only protection is the coloring that makes it resemble a wasp. Each of these animals
pretends to be something it is not, and it does this in
order to survive. Modern armies use camouflage to pro-
tect their soldiers, guns, ships, and military installations;
the result is proof positive of the defensive value of such
techniques. The reader will not be surprised then, if we
tell him that our subject has played a prominent part in
all discussions about the origin and the evolution of living organisms. Charles Darwin was one of the first to

stress the importance of camouflage, and since his day the subject has formed one of the strands of biological theory.

This is not to say that the authorities all agree. What some choose to explain as camouflage, others describe in altogether different terms. A host of experimenters has set out to prove the various theories, but always with perfect scientific detachment. The problem of mimicry, in particular, has become a veritable no man's land of biological battle.

These are things our book will explore. Casting our glance over a vast canvas, we shall try to trace the meaning of some of the colorful brush strokes that went into its painting.

I. CAMOUFLAGE AND VISION

The connection between camouflage and vision is so obvious that to discuss it is to run the risk of being trite. But any scientist who seeks a deeper understanding of the secrets of life must look into the obvious and question what others take for granted.

Camouflage implies a seeing eye from which to hide. Of course, hiding from your enemy is not the only way to deceive him—silence, too, can be an effective protection, and if the enemy is tracking you by scent he can be thrown off the trail. But camouflage is primarily a matter of seeing, because sight is our best sense; our eyes give us most of our information about our surroundings. Living forms strike us as being made for the living eye, just as food seems to be made for the digestive organs.

Let us take a quick look at some of the disguises used by familiar animals. "Disguise" and "display" are opposites. But opposites, far from being incompatible, are simply the two ends of the same field—here the field of vision. You have probably seen a particularly beautiful butterfly, say the peacock (*Vanessa io*), as it came to rest on a sunny stone (Fig. 1). Swiveling on its perch until the sun's rays strike it full on, the butterfly displays

FIG. 1.
The peacock butterfly
(*Vanessa io*)
flaunting its colors.

FIG. 2. The peacock butterfly in hiding.

its glorious wings—it is an exhibitionist. On another
occasion, when it is flying toward a wall, a tree trunk, or
a heap of foliage, the same butterfly will suddenly fold
its wings; as if by magic the colorful peacock disappears,
and in its place we find a leaf (Fig. 2). Here we have
display and disguise in the same creature; we say that
external appearance and behavior have a double role—
they are different under different conditions (dimorphic).
This change in appearance is characteristic of many butterflies whose upper and lower surfaces differ completely
—the Indian dead-leaf butterfly (*Kallima*) being an extreme case.

FIG. 3. The grasshopper (*Oedipoda germanica*) resting. The dark cross stripes have a camouflaging effect.

FIG. 4. The grasshopper taking off and displaying its dashing red hindwing.

In late summer or early autumn we may also meet the heavily camouflaged grasshopper (Fig. 3). When one of these musical fellows takes off, he displays a pair of radiant blue or red wings: like a ship, he has run up his flag (Fig. 4). A few yards farther, and the flag is struck again —once more our grasshopper is immobile and invisible. In his case too, self-effacement and display go hand in hand, and he can choose between them at will (Fig. 5).

Take also the case of birds. Here the distinction between brightness and drabness is often sexual: while the courting cock presents a magnificent spectacle, the brooding hen is camouflaged to delude her pursuers. In other

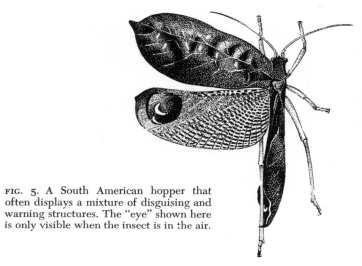

FIG. 5. A South American hopper that often displays a mixture of disguising and warning structures. The "eye" shown here is only visible when the insect is in the air.

birds, for example some shore birds, roles are reversed: the inconspicuous father sits on the eggs and rears the young while the handsome mother flits about oblivious of domestic duties. Then again, in pheasants the males and females alike may wear either the "feminine" disguise or else a party dress of splendid plumes. We must remember these examples if we are not to fall into the trap of giving our ideas ready-made labels.

Nor have we exhausted the list of sexual distinctions. Let us look at the duck. After the breeding season, the dashing, good-looking drake discards his glittering tuxedo for an unassuming tweed coat, not unlike his lady's everyday dress. To make matters even more complicated, both sexes have a brilliant wing mark, the so-called speculum, which is flashed as a signal when the bird takes flight. Once the wings are folded, the speculum recedes from view—another reminder of the close connection between spectacular color and humble disguise.

Clearly, the appearance of an animal is connected with its survival. Since it can seek protection both through concealment (cryptic coloration) and through sailing under a bright flag (warning coloring), the term "adaptive coloration" must be given the widest possible meaning.

II . SHAPE AND CAMOUFLAGE

1. *Markings That Blend with the Landscape*

Optical Illusions and the Laws of Vision

An optical illusion makes us feel that something has gone wrong with our senses and with our ability to judge things correctly. Modern Gestalt psychology has been able to show that optical illusions are the work of the eye itself; that, contrary to earlier opinions, the eye is the organizer rather than a passive receiver of impressions. In Figure 6a your eye will be struck by the symmetry of the figure as a whole and will have difficulty in picking out the set of isolated parts shown in Figure 6b. Clearly, certain forms attract our eyes far more strongly than do others.

FIG. 6. Regularity is in the eye of the beholder. We have difficulty picking out the system of lines shown in (b) although they are obviously parts of the total pattern. (After Metzger.)

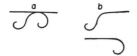

FIG. 7. The law of good form: we keep seeing (*a*) as a line and a curve and not as the patterns isolated in (*b*), which are equally well its parts.

Again, in Figure 7 (left) the eye is drawn along the straight line or the curve; we find it difficult to believe that the design comes from the two figures shown on the right. Psychologists have explained this by the so-called "law of good form."

This law is of first importance in camouflage. If an animal's markings "run on" into the background—its environment—the eye will follow the continuity and confuse the organism with its surroundings. The greater the number of such lines, spots, and stripes, the harder it is to make out the animal's outlines—its body has apparently dissolved. This concealing effect, called somatolysis, is very striking in the case of snakes. Some snakes stand out clearly when they are moving over a dull background, but when they keep still in colorful surroundings they simply disappear (Fig. 8).

Another example is provided by the nightjar, a bird with beautiful markings and feathers. The markings are emphasized when, as in Figure 9, the bird is held against a light background; in its breeding ground, however, the nightjar seems to merge completely with its environment, its colors and markings deceive the eye into identifying the bird with branches, leaves, pebbles, and odd shadows (Fig. 10). The ability to hold still is an essential part of camouflage, and when we remember how restless birds normally are we are amazed at the power of this instinct. Since holding still is particularly important in the survival of the young birds, it must be an inherited characteristic.

FIG. 8. The complicated pattern of the gaboon viper (*Bitis gabonica*) can attract attention or turn it away, depending on its background and its behavior. (Photograph taken at the Zurich Zoological Gardens by Beringer and Pampalucchi.)

FIG. 9. The European nightjar (*Caprimulgus europaeus*) is one of the most effectively camouflaged birds. Against the light background its vivid pattern is emphasized. (Photograph: H. R. Haefelfinger.)

FIG. 10. As the nightjar broods on the ground, it feels safe enough to yawn while being photographed. (Photograph: E. Hosking.)

Figure 11 shows how disguise can be combined with conspicuous markings for use on special occasions.

During the breeding and nesting periods most birds are quiet. At such times a protective cloak is doubly necessary (Fig. 12). Just as a good disguise demands immobility, so immobility needs an effective disguise. Investigators have paid much attention to the evolution of this double effect.

As the laws of vision are neutral, the law of good form, for instance, can either cause our eye to be turned away

FIG. 11. The nightjar flashing two flight signals, much as an airplane does. (Photograph: E. Hosking.)

from an animal or else to be attracted by it. Many butter-flies have independent patterns on forewings and hind-wings; this is conspicuous in butterfly collections in which the wings are unnaturally extended. Yet, in real life, the wings produce a quite deceptive symmetrical pattern (Fig. 13). This symmetry poses important genetic prob-lems which we shall examine more closely.

The Joining Effect

In the development of the embryo the original parts of an organ often arise in different parts of the body, gradually becoming organized into a whole. The rudi-mentary eye lens, for instance, arises some distance from the primary optic vesicles which eventually become the iris and the retina. The way in which separated parts come to form a whole—either an organ or a set of markings for disguise or display—has been called coaptation.

A good example of such an adjustment is found in tree frogs. East African types, such as *Megalixalus fornasinii,*

FIG. 12. Two young stone curlews (*Burhinus oedicnemus*) in sandy disguise. They hide by pressing tight to the ground—shortening their shadows. (Photograph: H. Traber.)

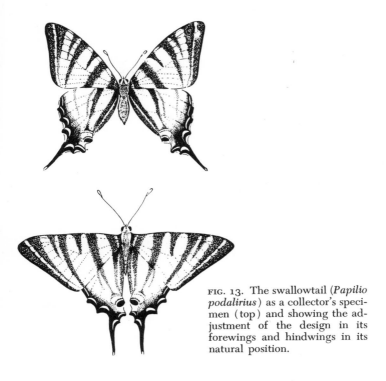

FIG. 13. The swallowtail (*Papilio podalirius*) as a collector's specimen (top) and showing the adjustment of the design in its forewings and hindwings in its natural position.

and South American kinds, like *Hyla leucophyllata,* are all alike, when leaping about, in presenting a brilliant patchwork of color and stripes. The moment they sit still on a leaf, however, extremities close to trunk, the isolated stripes fuse into a single dissolving pattern (Fig. 14). In the case of the East African tree frogs the final pattern is brown and shining silver, and these very contrasts provide excellent cover. H. B. Cott called this "coincident disruptive coloration," and I look upon it as just one aspect of the adjustment of separated parts to each other (coaptation).

FIG. 14. A South American tree frog (*Hyla leucophyllata*) in resting position. Its closed pattern dissolves its outline pattern into its background. (After Cott.)

The same phenomenon can be observed in the case of the common frog also, though here it is restricted to the animal's hind legs, where, when the frog is at rest, dark bands run across the folded limb, producing a surprisingly co-ordinated result (Fig. 15). Here, too, the individual pieces of the final pattern began in different rudiments, and only in the rest position do the frog's markings have their dissembling effect.

In the development of the butterfly wings, the caterpillar's second and third segments are tiny rudiments of the wings with all their wonderful patterns (Fig. 16). These cells develop only during the last stages of the caterpillar's life, the individual scales of the final wing patterns being formed later still, during the chrysalis stage. Yet long before this happens, the final pattern must have been "determined" in the young caterpillar! Clearly, the final pattern must have been inherent in the separate rudiments.

The adjustment of forewings and hindwings is particularly clear in living butterflies at rest. We have already seen that dead specimens are usually pinned to display the greatest wing spread, thus cloaking the effect of the parts on the whole. Displays of dead butterflies have been largely responsible for the fact that this has been overlooked for so long.

FIG. 15. Many frog patterns, in the resting position, merge into bands running across the entire folded leg and foot, so that the frogs disappear into their surroundings.

FIG. 16. Rudimentary wings appear in caterpillars as separate folds within the thorax. In the diagram they are shown in section.

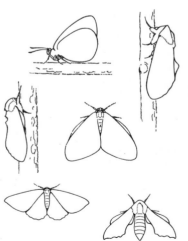

FIG. 17. Butterflies and moths in rest position, displaying varying amounts of lower wing. The color of the visible part matches with the upper-wing color. Top: butterfly and brown moth. Center: brown moth and geometrid moth. Bottom: Geometrid moth and hawkmoth. (After Oudemans.)

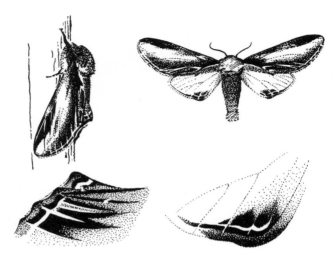

FIG. 18. Pattern adjustment of the swallow prominent (*Pheosia tremula*). The small pattern on the hindwing (bottom right magnified) matches the pattern at the edge of the forewing (bottom left). (After Oudemans.)

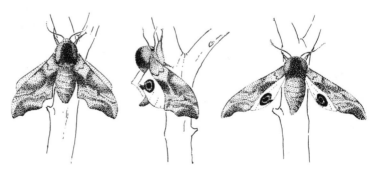

FIG. 19. Hawk-moth (*Smerinthus ocellatus*) exhibiting the eyes of its lower wing. These visible parts of the wing in the rest position are concealingly colored (left). (After Japha.)

Moths and butterflies at rest often expose a small area of the otherwise hidden wing (Fig. 17). Thus, many butterflies close their wings to expose a small part of the underside of the forewing; bombycid moths expose a ridge of the frontal or else part of the anal margin of the hindwing; and hawk-moths show both the frontal and the anal edge of the hindwing.

Like its relatives, the swallow prominent (*Pheosia tremula*) is effectively disguised once its wings are folded (Fig. 18). In profile it displays a toothed edge which looks like part of the forewing, when in fact it is the anal angle of the hindwing, from the rest of which it differs in color. A miscroscopic examination reveals that this marginal zone fits exactly with the exposed area. A similar co-ordination of parts is seen in the rest position of the hawk-moth (*Smerinthus ocellatus*). Here the hindwings with their lovely eyespots have a frontal margin that is the color of bark, and this margin alone is exposed when the moth is at rest (Fig. 19).

Maximum Broken-Color Effects

The concealing patterns are considerably more effective when they appear with strongly contrasted tones (Fig. 20) which turn attention away from other details and especially from the animal's contours. Now, while such maximum contrast may be a particularly effective device for breaking up the animal's outline, it may equally well produce the opposite effect—of emphasizing outlines. Once again the effect varies from case to case (Fig. 21).

We might mention another side of our problem: adaptive behavior. As the wind shakes the leaves of an aspen at the edge of a wood, the tree suddenly emerges from the forest wall. The wall was an optical illusion based on the rhythmic movement of the individual trees. When animals make use of this fact, their behavior is called adaptive. Not surprisingly, adaptive behavior is com-

FIG. 20. Dissolving boundary contrast in the oak egger (*Lasio-campa quercus*). (Photograph: D. Widmer.)

monest in animals of dark, concealing color. Thus, when the bittern is alarmed it becomes quite rigid. Tilting its body upward till the beak points to the sky, the russet and black streaks of its plumage blending perfectly with the surrounding reeds, the bittern is indistinguishable from its environment. In this position it will keep swiveling toward the observer, gazing at him fixedly with a glassy eye. Should a gust of wind cause the reeds to sway, the bird will sway rhythmically with them.

Adaptive behavior is common to many marine fishes resembling seaweed, to certain types of fresh-water fishes that float down-river like dead leaves, and to stick insects (Phasmidae) which can make abdominal contortions in rhythm with the leaves among which they live.

The pleasure of discovering the confusing dissolving patterns often causes naturalists to overlook their complex nature. Seeing disguises at every turn, they insist on describing as concealing, or "cryptic," the most scream-

FIG. 21. Maximum contrasting tones in butterfly wings.

ing of colors and the most spectacular of patterns (Fig. 22). Some have even called the zebra's stripes dissolving effects, thus contradicting every hunter's personal experience. Similarly, they describe the brilliant stripes of some tropical fishes as having these effects. True, the markings divide the fish's body into different fields, but such fields look more conspicuous against the monotonous background of the sea. Not surprisingly then, the beautiful clownfish (*Amphiprion percula*) takes refuge among large sea anemones where—in spite of its striking colors —it is safe from pursuit (Fig. 23). Only an examination of an animal's total behavior can decide whether its particular markings are concealing or warning.

FIG. 22.
Maximum contrasting
tones in the gazelle.

FIG. 23. The flashing clownfish (*Amphiprion percula*) lives close to sea anemones to hide his brilliant colors in their tentacles.

FIG. 24. The plover's eggs may be camouflaged and yet conspicuous because of shadows cast when the sun is low in the sky. (Photograph: H. Traber.)

2. Concealment of Contours

Concealment of Shadows

The white coat of the polar hare does little to conceal the animal when its shadow can be seen for miles against the white snow. The most dissolving of patterns is useless in the wrong kind of light (Figs. 24 and 25).

This drawback is overcome by what we may call the "Peter Pan effect," that is, by not having a shadow. Clearly, the closer an animal crouches to the ground, the smaller its shadow. The same effect can be produced by lateral flaps cr projections (Fig. 26). Good examples of animals that crouch are young stone curlews, squids, and many reptiles. In insects flattening may be produced by special flanges (Fig. 27), or else, as in many geometrid moths, by pressing the wings close to the support.

FIG. 25. The disguise of the hawk-moth (*Dilina tiliae*) impaired by a strong shadow. (Photograph: D. Widmer.)

FIG. 26. Shadows may be hidden by flaps or flanges.

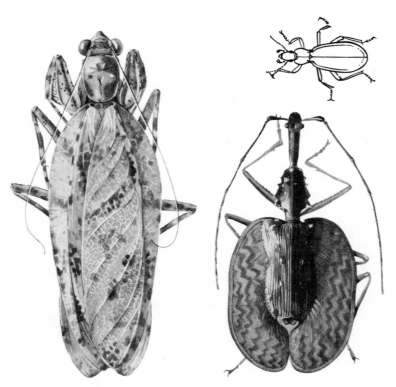

FIG. 27. Left: The Indo-Malayan relative of the praying mantis (*Theopompa*) looks as if it had been squashed.
FIG. 28. Right: Carabid beetles have flattened wing covers.

Not all shadow-concealing flaps are protective, some carabid beetles, for instance, having a marked flattening of the hard wing cases (Fig. 28), even though these insects normally live under cover.

Fleshy tubercles along the shadow-forming edges cause many animals to look like natural outgrowths of their support. The best examples are bark-dwelling geckos and geometrid moth larvae (Fig. 29).

A different application of the Peter Pan effect is used by racing crabs, animals that are so well camouflaged that they would be completely invisible did not their shadows betray them as they run about on the beach. When they feel threatened, these crabs make for footprints or similar hollows in the sand, where they can hide their shadows.

Shadows can also be obliterated or reduced by active body orientation. Thus, the female standard-winged

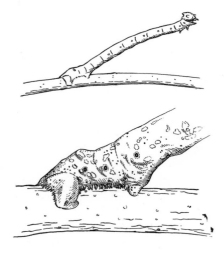

FIG. 29. Geometrid moth caterpillars, often called measuring worms (for example, *Pachys betularia*), combine more than one camouflage: rigid posture, concealing colors, and shadow-disguising tubercles. (After a photograph by Cott.)

nightjar (*Macrodipteryx longipennis*) of Nigeria, which nests on the ground, will keep swiveling toward the sun so as to keep its shadow as small as possible. This is clearly one form of "sun worship" that has great survival value.

Some butterflies will come to rest so that the shadow of their upturned wings is reduced to a very thin line, and others will tilt their bodies to one side until the shadow is hidden beneath the wing surface. The angle of tilt in *Satyrus semele* can be as much as forty or even fifty degrees. Experiments have shown that like the crouching of birds such tilting is purely protective. The most striking example of wing-tilting is the British green hairstreak butterfly (*Thecla rubi*), which can tilt its body so much to one side that its green undersurface appears to lie flat on the leaf on which the hairstreak has settled.

The war against treacherous shadows can be waged with other weapons as well, as when the shadows cast by the veins of leaves, by bark, or by blades of grass are suggested by misleading patterns and surfaces.

Counter-shading

Another method of doing away with shadow effects is counter-shading (or Thayer's principle). If we paint a cylinder or sphere in graded tints of gray, the darkest

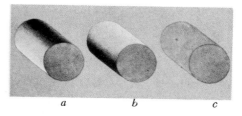

a   *b*   *c*

FIG. 30. Thayer's principle of counter-shading. (*a*) Counter-shaded cylinder uniformly illuminated, (*b*) unshaded cylinder with top lighting, (*c*) the combined effect of counter-shading and top lighting.

part facing toward the source of light, and the lightest away from it, the body's own shade so balances this color scheme that the outlines become dissolved (Fig. 30). Such graded tints are typical of vertebrates (Fig. 31) and of many other animals.

Counter-shading is particularly effective in surroundings which break up shadows, for example, in long grass or woods, and its protective effect is especially important to relatively defenseless animals. It is therefore not surprising that many smaller types of animals have retained this contour-dissolving distribution of color during the thousands of years in which selective processes have influenced their evolution. The stronger a mammal or bird, the more it can deviate from counter-shading without harmful effect. Thus, many of the larger animals com-

FIG. 31.
Counter-shading is typical
of vertebrates.

FIG. 32. "Two-surface effect." (*a*) Cylinder with two regions counter-shaded separately in diffuse light, (*b*) unpainted cylinder with top lighting, (*c*) two-surface effect with top lighting: contours disappear.

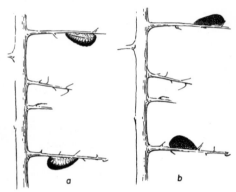

FIG. 33. Light experiments with caterpillars (*Papilio podalirius*). (*a*) Under unexpected top lighting, (*b*) adjusted to top lighting. (After Süffert.)

bine counter-shading with maximum broken-color contrast on the back and with conspicuous patterns near the head or tail.

Fishes often show a modification of counter-shading: the back may be blue, while the underside is silver. Clearly, this corresponds to the fact that the sea is below and the sky above.

Now, even before Thayer formulated his famous principle of counter-shading, Poulton had observed the same effect in moths and butterflies in the cocoon stage. The whole problem was carefully reinvestigated some thirty years ago. H. Süffert discovered the existence of double counter-shading in caterpillars of the clouded yellow butterfly (*Colias edusa*), in which two regions of the body—separated by light contrast—are counter-shaded independently (Fig. 32). This double counter-shading only has a contour-dissolving effect when the light comes from the top and when it goes hand in hand with an appropriate attitude. Süffert was able to show experimentally that the caterpillar always turns toward a source of light so as to have its back lighted. Figure 33 illustrates an illumination experiment with the green caterpillar of *Papilio podalirius*. Clearly, the animal's attitude decides the optical result.

Other insects are counter-shaded for ventral illumination, as for instance, the caterpillars of the hawk-moth (Fig. 34), or the caterpillars of a South Asiatic moth (*Actias selene*) in which ventral illumination produces double counter-shading effects (Figs. 35 and 36). Süffert

FIG. 34. Caterpillar of the hawk-moth (*Smerinthus ocellatus*) showing the relation between an upside-down position and inverted counter-shading. Top: the normal rest position; bottom: the same reversed. (After Cott.)

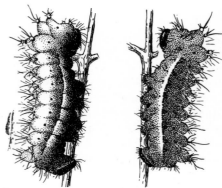

FIG. 35. A caterpillar of a Southeast Asian geometrid moth (*Actias selene*) lighted from the belly side (right), showing dissolving two-surface effect. In artificial light (left) the contours are overemphasized. (After Süffert.)

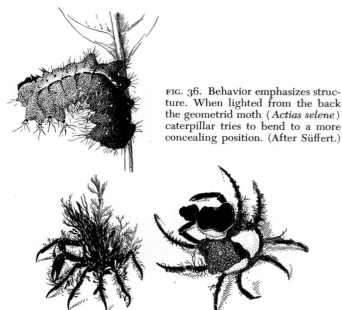

FIG. 36. Behavior emphasizes structure. When lighted from the back the geometrid moth (*Actias selene*) caterpillar tries to bend to a more concealing position. (After Süffert.)

FIG. 37. Two masked crabs: left, *Hyas,* camouflaged with algae; right, *Pisa,* covered with sponges and corals.

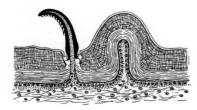

FIG. 38. Section through the horny shell of a masked crab showing bristles for holding material. (After Aurivillius.)

has been able to show that the turning of these animals toward the light is not due to visual responses but to responses of the insect's entire surface.

3. *Camouflage Through Masking*

Ever since marine aquaria were first used for scientific investigations, naturalists have been interested in a small group of exceptional crabs (of the genera *Hyas, Maia, Pisa, Inachus, Stenorhynchus,* and related types) which are camouflaged with algae, sponges, and colonies of polyps (Fig. 37). In this way the crabs completely merge with their natural background.

Since many barnacle-like creatures (Cirripedes) make their home on the crab's bony covering, we might be inclined to dismiss its effective disguise as purely accidental, but on closer examination we realize that the crab is one of nature's shrewdest camouflage specialists—the "natural growth" proves to be a deliberate masquerade.

The mask is worn quite loosely. If we remove it carefully, the crab will soon replace it with new material. The crab's carapace cover is supplied with a dense array of elastic horny bristles hooked at the tips, which, unlike the rest of the armor, are eminently suited to holding camouflage objects (Fig. 38). These bristles are found only in masking crabs.

The foreign material is squeezed on by means of pincers (chelae) that are much more agile than those of other crabs and that can reach all the bristles (Fig. 39). Hand in hand with this type of camouflage goes another physical peculiarity: the body is laterally narrowed (Fig. 40) and lacks the horny plates at the sides of other crabs. In consequence, the legs can move about far more freely.

So much for the structure. As for the appropriate behavior, all we know is that the crab uses its pincers for picking off small algae and cutting sponges to exactly the required size. The crab then puts these into its mouth and chews them for a few seconds before rubbing them firmly on its body. Should any of the substances fall off, they are popped back into the mouth and chewed again. No doubt they are covered with a sticky secretion in the process of chewing, for the crab neither swallows nor changes the shape of the particles.

If this "mask" is pulled off the crab, it becomes very restless and rushes about in search of a new disguise. Each kind of crab has its own masking method: thus *Maia verrucosa* always starts with the head and often leaves it at that, and *Posidonia* lengthens the head—and thus the whole body—by applying strips of material, while *Inachus scorpio* only camouflages its first pair of

FIG. 39. The pincers of a masked crab (*Hyas*) are extremely agile and can reach every part of the body that is covered with bristles. (After Aurivillius.)

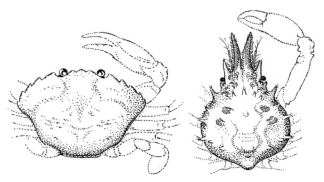

FIG. 40. A swimming crab (*Portunus*), left, contrasted with a masked crab (*Pisa*). (After Aurivillius.)

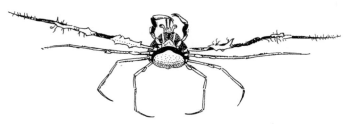

FIG. 41. Only the first pair of walking legs of this masked crab (*Inachus scorpio*) can be camouflaged.

very long walking legs, which are then inclined at an angle to the other legs (Fig. 41).

An entirely different kind of disguise is used by the sponge crab (*Dromia vulgaris,* Fig. 42). This crab, after cutting out its colorful sponge mask, holds it in place over its back by a specially modified last pair of legs which are shorter and carried up higher than the other ones (Fig. 43). The sponge crab is an expert cutter, for if we offer it a large piece of wet paper it will immediately cut out a piece of just the right size. If its paper coat should fall off, it will quickly design a fresh one.

Crabs are not the only animals to use foreign matter as disguise. Many insects, and particularly their larvae,

FIG. 42. A sponge crab (*Dromia vulgaris*) holding its sponge mask by a specially adapted pair of legs. (Partly after Fenizia.)

mask their unprotected bodies by a cover that is part glandular secretion and part foreign body. Good examples are the family of bombycid moths (Psychidae), and the aquatic caddis fly. Foreign substances may be allowed to stick to the skin or else the larvae may hide beneath their own excrement. The predatory larva of the lacewing fly (*Chrysopa*) covers itself with the remains of dead ants, and if these are taken off, it quickly renews its coat.

Another mask is one of nature's strangest disguises: the white froth or cuckoo spit which is the hiding place for the larvae of many sucking insects (Homoptera), for example, the common froghopper, and which is made up of intestinal and glandular juices mixed with the air they blow through their air tubes.

All these protective devices are characteristic of the larval stage, the longest phase of the insect's life cycle, thus ensuring the greatest protection for the species.

While on the subject of secretion, we must mention a most highly differentiated animal form—the squid. Everyone knows that squids can emit a dense smoke screen when pursued, but only few of us have read L. Cuénot's fascinating description of the behavior of *Sepiola:* "In the summer, *Sepiola* is almost invisible against the shal-

FIG. 43. A sponge crab (*Dromia vulgaris*) without its sponge, showing the modified last pair of legs. (After Fenizia.)

low and sandy background of its native bays. But the moment anyone approaches, the animal darkens and ejects a small cloud of dense ink. The cloud remains in *Sepiola*'s original position, while the animal itself moves two or three yards sideways where, its former bright self again, it becomes invisible once more. *Sepiola* will continue to elude a pursuer until such time as its ink supply is exhausted." Clearly, in expelling just enough coloring matter to simulate its own contours, this cuttlefish shows a very delicate sense of proportion.

A special disguise is used by some gastropod mollusks (for example, *Xenophora*): the shell is hidden under a spiral of shells and pebbles (Fig. 44). Only the underside and entrance are left free so that the mollusk's movements are unimpeded. The carrier snail (*Xenophora*) uses its foot for gripping objects and also for jumping by rapid contractions. The foot is thus well suited to finding and holding future additions to the shell. Some of these snails prefer the shells and shell fragments of other mollusks, while others like pebbles. Naturalists have humorously used the names "conchologist" and "mineralogist" to describe the carrier snails. In the early stages this collecting passion is quite absent—the larger the animal grows, the bigger its hoard. However, some types are

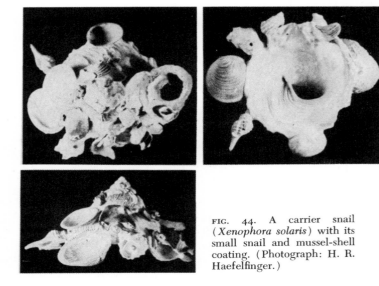

FIG. 44. A carrier snail (*Xenophora solaris*) with its small snail and mussel-shell coating. (Photograph: H. R. Haefelfinger.)

poor collectors and completely discontinue the habit in later life. Occasionally, we find very symmetrical patterns that lead us to believe the animal must be capable of selecting and examining the foreign matter, and in some fossilized shells the collected substances are purely ornamental.

In a very striking snail (Fig. 45) in which some of the whorls have been covered with small shells in early life, the mantle continues its work differently: as calcium is excreted from time to time, marginal spikes are pushed out. At first the spikes are small and irregular, but later they become more and more symmetrical. Spikes are merely a variation of the function of the mantle, which normally gives rise to the many types of mollusk shells. This particular snail (*Xenophora solaris*) is *not* a camouflaged mollusk. It interests us for that very reason. The very difference from its relatives illustrates the fact that

FIG. 45. Left: a carrier snail (*Xenophora*) with shells; right: a snail (*Xenophora solaris*) with calcium spikes and with shells added during earlier stages. (Photograph: H. R. Haefelfinger.)

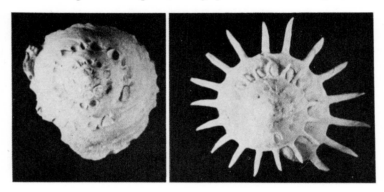

camouflage is but one of a wide range of different functions in one and the same field. In mollusks this field stretches from marginal spikes to the selection of foreign matter—from pure ornamentation to complete disguise.

4. Camouflage Through Resemblance

In the most effective camouflage the animal's contours dissolve and take on a special resemblance to other animals or objects. This is called mimetic resemblance.

Leaf Resemblance

The green carpet which covers such vast regions of the earth is the home of countless animals, many of which have in fact adopted a protective leaf disguise. Because it illustrates some of the basic principles of camouflage, we shall examine this disguise in some detail.

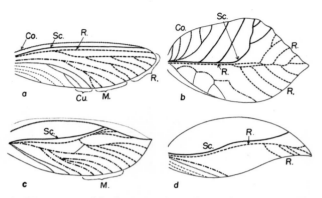

FIG. 46. Wing veins of leaf insects. (*a*) Of a Carboniferous insect (*Palaeodictyoptera*), (*b*) of a tropical grasshopper (*Mimetica*), (*c*) of a grasshopper (*Cyrtophyllites*) of the Jurassic period, (*d*) of another grasshopper (*Mastiphaga*). The displacement of the subcostal and radial veins to the center of the "leaf," produces a "midrib." *Co:* costal vein; *Cu:* cubital margin; *M:* median; *R:* radial vein and branches; *Sc:* subcostal vein.

Leaves are usually flat, crisscrossed by veins, and have an oval and often a toothed edge—the very shape of many an insect's wing. Some insects, therefore, need only show their wings in profile (Fig. 46) to be mistaken for leaves.

Straight-winged insects, the Orthoptera, with thin, notched wings whose veins seemed to be built round a midrib, appeared approximately 300 million years ago, as long ago as the Carboniferous period, when our familiar types of leafy tree were not yet in existence. Clearly, leaflike animals are as old as the hills.

The leaf resemblance is greatly increased when the marginal veins are shifted to a central position to form a central axis which looks like a midrib from which the other veins branch off (Fig. 46*b*). Moths and butterflies whose veins are not shifted may fold their wings in such a way as to simulate this typical leaf venation. Here color plays the part of the veins, and the leaf resemblance is increased further by stalklike projections on the hind-wings. The Asiatic dead-leaf butterfly (*Kallima*) is the classic example of this type of leaf resemblance (Fig. 47).

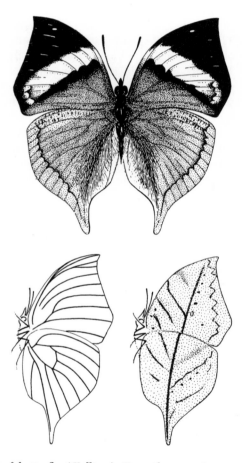

FIG. 47. The dead-leaf butterfly (*Kallima*). Top: the conspicuous upper surface; bottom left: the real direction of the veins; and bottom right: the superimposed pattern. (Partly after Süffert.)

Geometrid moths have their own way of imitating leaves. For instance, a South American kind (*Oxidia*, Fig. 48) exhibits its upper side, which has a pronounced central stripe, adding greatly to the desired effect, as the moth settles on a branch in its typical position.

Special mention must be made of the walking leaf (*Phyllium*), an Australian orthopterous insect (Fig. 49). The walking leaf differs from our other examples in that only the female, which is unable to fly, resembles a leaf. The airborne male is smaller and has typical shortened wing covers, with a centrally placed radial vein (Fig. 50). In the female all the principal veins are displaced to form a conspicuous "midrib," and in the adult the "midribs" of two corresponding wing covers and the subsidiary veins combine to look like the characteristic veins of leaves. The effect is further increased through the flattening of the leg segments. The earliest stages of the walking leaf show a vivid red—only the adult is a leaf insect proper.

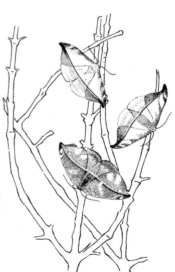

FIG. 48. The leaf resemblance of a South American geometrid moth (*Oxidia*) is increased by a "midrib" running across all four wings. (After Picado.)

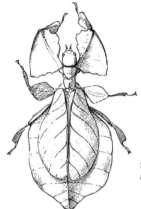

FIG. 49. The walking leaf (*Phyllium siccifolium*).

General resemblance to leaves is, of course, enhanced by a green or light-brown color (Fig. 51). The deception can be increased by further modifications. Thus, the dead-leaf butterfly (*Kallima*), for instance, displays transparent or white spots that look like fungi, and some South American grasshoppers exhibit skeletonized leaf effects, fungus growths, and typical leaf discolorations. Some wings even resemble leaves that have been bitten through by caterpillars (Fig. 52). Only the careful examination and comparison of both fully extended wings will reveal the symmetrical arrangement of these indentations.

Similar effects can be observed in many butterflies, for example in *Draconia rusina*, which lives in Guiana (Fig. 53). Not only are its wings deeply indented, but they have patches that look as if some disease had attacked them. Leaf venation is here represented by special wing scales, the wings themselves lacking an appropriate vein structure.

Resemblance to leaves is not restricted to insects. In the lower Amazon Valley there lives a fish (*Monocirrhus polyacanthus*, Fig. 54) whose popular Brazilian name is

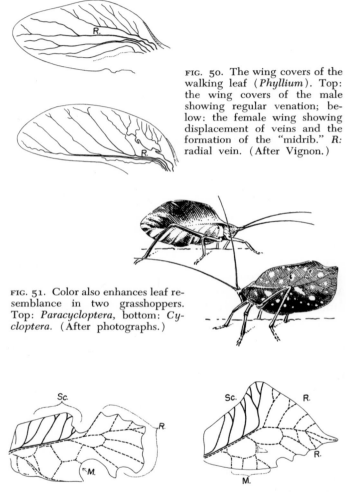

FIG. 50. The wing covers of the walking leaf (*Phyllium*). Top: the wing covers of the male showing regular venation; below: the female wing showing displacement of veins and the formation of the "midrib." *R:* radial vein. (After Vignon.)

FIG. 51. Color also enhances leaf resemblance in two grasshoppers. Top: *Paracycloptera*, bottom: *Cycloptera*. (After photographs.)

FIG. 52. Wings of two tropical South American grasshoppers (*Typophyllum*) which look as if they had been chewed by insects. (See Fig. 46 for key.)

FIG. 53. Leaf imitation of a South American butterfly (*Draconia rusina*) with "damaged" wings and skeletonized leaf effects. (After Cott.)

FIG. 54. The South American leaf fish (*Monocirrhus polyacanthus*). (After Cott.)

peche de folha ("leaf fish"). It either hangs head downward beneath the surface of the water, or else it lies flat on the bottom of the river, where it is hidden among dead foliage. Even when caught in a net, the fish remains quite motionless—clearly its behavior, too, is leaflike. The resemblance is in fact so great that leaves must be netted and carefully examined if the "leaf fish" is to be picked out.

The fish attains its leaf shape by a strong lateral compression and by the fact that it flattens its transparent dorsal and anal fins tight against the body. The coloration aids the deceptive effect. The fish does not move by lateral strokes of the body and tail that one can see, but by rapid undulations of the almost invisible dorsal and anal fins. The "dead leaf" is a perpetual trap. The moment a smaller fish approaches, the "leaf" opens its relatively large mouth and swallows the victim with one huge gulp.

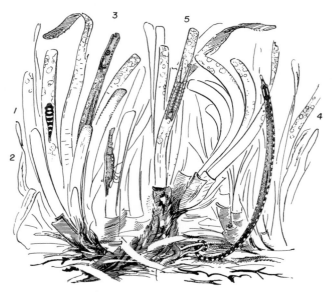

FIG. 55. Among Mediterranean sea grasses (*Posidonia caulinii*):
(1) Limpet (*Lepadogaster*), (2) prawn (*Hippolyte*), (3) pipefish
(*Siphonostoma*), (4) pipefish (*Nerophis*), (5) isopod (*Idothea*).
The leaves are covered with coralline algae (*Melobesia*) often imitated by animals. (Partly after Bauer.)

The oceans, too, abound with plants and appropriately
disguised animals. The higher marine plants have real
leaves, for example the sea grasses (*Zostera* and *Posidonia*), which form submarine meadows in coastal regions
where a sandy bottom allows them to take root. Here,
many fishes resemble their swaying and slender leaves.
Pipefishes (*Syngnathus, Nerophis*) achieve a leaf effect
through swimming vertically, their heads directed upward
(Fig. 55).

On rocky coasts the dense undergrowth of algae har-
bors a whole host of camouflaged animals (Fig. 56),
first and foremost among which are a number of marine

snails (opisthobranchiates) with short disappearing flaps or flanges. Examples are the green *Elysia* snail and the sea hare (*Aplysia*) whose color may be red, olive green, or dark brown, according to age. This is because the young sea hare prefers to live amid red algae, and the adult prefers brown. Young sea hares retain their redness even when placed next to brown algae; the agreement between their color and their environment is obviously the result of choice. Some crustaceans, too—particularly a grotesque shrimp (Caprellidae)—are extremely well camouflaged to resemble their habitat of algae, polyps, and moss coral (Fig. 57).

Even fishes sometimes resemble the algae of their immediate environment. The Australian sea dragon (*Phyllopteryx eques*), which is related to the sea horse, carries this resemblance to extreme lengths by wearing what look like branches of a fine weed (Fig. 58).

FIG. 56. Marine snails among sea grasses and algae. Left to right: *Lobiger serradifalci, Elysia viridis,* and a young sea hare (*Aplysia punctata*).

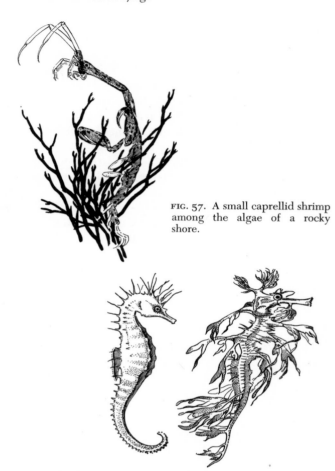

FIG. 57. A small caprellid shrimp among the algae of a rocky shore.

FIG. 58. A sea horse (*Hippocampus*) and its superbly camouflaged relative, the Pacific sea dragon (*Phyllopteryx eques*).

FIG. 59. A frogfish (*Histrio histrio*), which is particularly well camouflaged, lives amid the sargassum.

In frogfishes, both form and color combine to produce a most astonishing likeness to seaweed. This is particularly the case with "the actor" (*Histrio*), which carries on its hidden life amid the golden sargassum (Fig. 59). Related species live amid the coral reefs, and all of them are experts at performing the vanishing trick.

Resemblance to Bark, Twigs, and Lichen

While some animals resemble leaves, others prefer to imitate bark. All flat surfaces are as if made for this purpose, and many moths, particularly the geometrids, have but to spread their wings to resemble the trees on which they come to rest. Others, for instance hawk-moths, simply hide their conspicuous hindwings (Fig. 60). In certain bugs, such as the Brazilian pentatomid bug (*Phloea*), the seemingly squashed body segments produce a most remarkable disguise (Fig. 61).

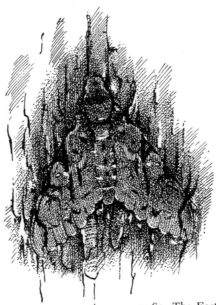

FIG. 60. The East African hawk-moth (*Xanthopan m. morgani*) looks like bark. (After Cott.)

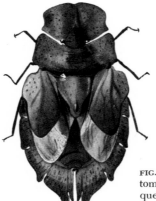

FIG. 61. A South American pentatomid bug (*Phloea corticata*) masquerading as a flake of bark.

Tree geckos show similar flattening effects, particularly of the tail, a fact on which we remarked in discussing shadow elimination; and many tropical snakes have their heads so modified that the tip looks like a twig (Fig. 62). The most striking resemblance to bark is provided by the plumage of birds that imitate entire branches, brown feathers with broken cross patterns and irregular patches greatly contributing to the disappearance of their contours. Needless to say, even the most perfect imitations fail in the absence of appropriate behavior patterns.

We have already mentioned that master of camouflage, the nightjar. How many factors must interact before camouflage is complete is best illustrated by a related bird, the frogmouth (*Batrachostomus*) from Sumatra (Fig. 63). Its appearance, or rather its disappearance, is a combination of barklike color with mottled patches, maximum disruptive contrast, and dotted feather tips.

FIG. 62. The strange deformation of the heads of Malagasy tree snakes. Top: *Langaha intermedia*, bottom: *Langaha alluaudi*.

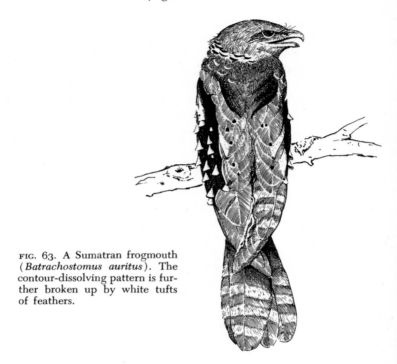

FIG. 63. A Sumatran frogmouth (*Batrachostomus auritus*). The contour-dissolving pattern is further broken up by white tufts of feathers.

Furthermore, special white tufts help to break up the contours. Our illustration places the bird against an unnatural background the better to illustrate the symmetry of even so pronounced a contour-dissolving pattern.

The American nightjar (*Nyctibius griseus*), popularly called the poor-me-one, or common potoo (Fig. 64), is well known for its doleful song and its excellent disguise. Here, bark resemblance is coupled with a rigid posture that simulates a broken branch. The illustration (Fig. 64, right) shows this bird caught unawares in a beam of light. The symmetry of the pattern and the large eye easily give the bird away. It would never take up this position during the day, when it invariably assumes a rigid posture, the open beak and eyelid resembling cracks in the bark, and the wings and tail looking like part of a branch (Fig. 64, left). The bird seems to be part of the tree on which it perches, and it keeps its rigid posture even during brooding.

Resemblance to branches and to bark may be restricted to the most helpless—the earliest—period in a bird's life. Thus, the Indian tree swift (*Hemiprocne longipennis*), which is a powerful flier, has no need for protective coloration once the wings are fully developed. Its young are reared in dangerously small nests (36mm × 22mm) that are fastened precariously to branches and hold just one egg. The young elude marauders by their remarkable resemblance to bark and by a posture very similar to that of the nightjar. This bark coloring disappears, however, with the first molt.

Other animals imitate the different lichen patterns that appear on bark, rock, and walls. Moths and caterpillars,

FIG. 64. The common potoo, or poor-me-one (*Nyctibius griseus*); left: in the daytime; right: surprised at night. (After photographs.)

FIG. 65. The nest of the long-tailed titmouse
(*Aegithalos caudatus*), expertly camouflaged with lichen. (Photograph: H. Traber.)

beetles, straight-winged insects, spiders, geckos, and tree
frogs have been known to use this method of enjoying a
particularly effective disguise, and many birds camouflage their nests by covering them with lichen (Fig. 65).
The animal which carries this type of resemblance to its
extremes is the Malagasy weevil (*Lithinus nigrocristatus*)
of Madagascar (Fig. 66). The buff-tip moth (*Phalera
bucephala*) combines bark and lichen patterns with a
branch-stump effect that is extremely deceptive (Fig.

FIG. 66. The Malagasy weevil (*Lithinus nigrocristatus*) resembles lichen.

67). Even greater is the bark-lichen resemblance of the Malagasy bug (*Flatoides dealbatus*) whose flattened wing covers bear conspicuous lichen markings (Fig. 68).

The caterpillars of many Lepidoptera have become famous for their resemblance to twigs. Keeping stock-still and with the body held outward at an angle from the support, these animals make the maximum use of their concealing coloration. The abdominal legs have become reduced to two pairs, as a result of which the geometrid moth caterpillar moves along with the looping gait which has earned it the name of "measuring worm" or "looper" (Fig. 29). Here the animal is concealed not so much by its appearance as by its concealing attitude. A few of the many possible attitudes of geometrid moth larvae are illustrated in Figure 69. Naturally, concealing patterns go a long way to increase the effectiveness of such behavior.

FIG. 67. The buff-tip moth (*Phalera bucephala*) combining bark and lichen pattern with branch-stump effect.

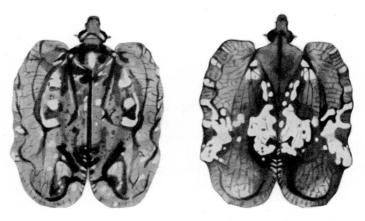

FIG. 68. The Malagasy bug (*Flatoides dealbatus*) combining lichen pattern with shadow-eliminating flaps.

FIG. 69. Geometrid moth caterpillars (*Eupithecia*) with particularly concealing patterns and attitudes. *E. scabiosata* on scabious, *E. nanata* on heather, and *E. schiefereri* on toadflax. (After Dietze.)

Another method of twig resemblance is practiced by some twig insects (such as *Parasosibia parva*), which rest on a branch with head downward and with the antennae and front legs pressed closely to the stem (Fig. 70). The rest of the body is pushed away from the support at a sharp angle and looks very much like a twig. An Australian grasshopper *Zabrochilus australis*) is an even better deceiver. Like *Parasosibia* it takes an upside-down position, but its resemblance to a twig is due to its wings alone (Fig. 70).

Insects and birds can also imitate the appearance of branches, thorns, reeds, and many other plants (Figs. 71, 72, 73).

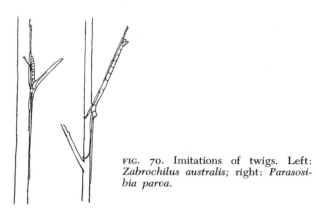

FIG. 70. Imitations of twigs. Left: *Zabrochilus australis;* right: *Parasosibia parva.*

Special Protective and Aggressive Resemblance

We might easily be misled into believing that the only means of camouflage is imitation of the support or background. However, this is not the case—predators often lure their prey by resembling harmless and desirable objects.

Mantids have refined this kind of disguise to a remarkable extent (Fig. 74). Thus, the female of a Burmese mantid (*Gongylus trachelophyllus*), while otherwise of typical build, has a petal-like protothorax. The underside of this is shaded a delicate lavender which gradually turns pink at the edges. Some naturalists tell us that they have also observed ornamental patches, but these disappear when the specimen is dead. A central brown spot completes the flower effect. Since only the underside is marked the insect must stretch its thorax and throw back its head in order to exhibit its flower display in the brightest possible light. The forelegs are kept in the usual folded position typical of the praying mantis. Occasionally, the insect will sway its abdomen from side to side. Just as butterflies settle in bright sunlight, so this

FIG. 71. A lacewing (*Drepanopteryx phalaenoides*) whose conceal-ing pattern and wing shape provide excellent camouflage anywhere.

FIG. 72. The plume moth looks like part of a plant. (Photograph: D. Widmer.)

FIG. 73. The Southeast Asian mantid
(*Toxodera denticulata*) camouflaged
to resemble bark and twigs.

mantid always places her floral breast toward the sun and
into the brightest light—the rest of her, especially the
peculiarly flattened legs, resembles dead foliage. The
floral color appears very early in her life, but the central
spot only reaches its final position after the sixth molting.
The male's disguise is but a pale reflection of his mate's,
but then it is she who catches the small, flower-loving
insects.

Hunting is not the only function of this conspicuous
color scheme. If this female mantid is threatened, for
instance if we push a finger close to her, she will suddenly change position and raise her front legs to flash
her red, white, and blue warning colors at us. This is the
threatening attitude, intended to frighten enemies. Other

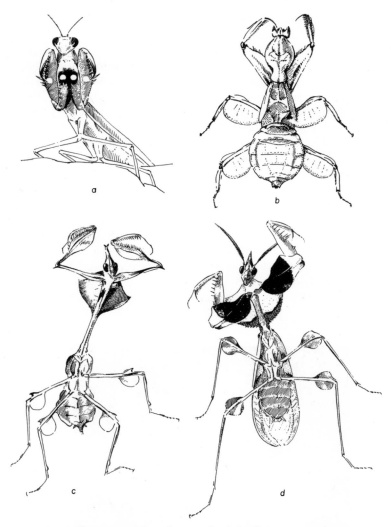

FIG. 74. Different attitudes of mantids. (*a*) Threatening position displaying eyespots, (*b*) early stage of *Hymenopus coronatus* with petal-like limb structures, (*c*) *Gongylus trachelophyllus* (Southeast Asia) in threatening attitude, (*d*) *Idolum diabolicum* (East Africa) in threatening attitude.

mantids display conspicuous eyespots beneath their forelegs (Fig. 74*a*).

Our Burmese mantid is of such great interest because
it is an example of alluring and threatening features combined. The same combination of effects is characteristic
of many animals and may mislead investigators. Thus,
naturalists are not sure whether an African relative
(*Idolum diabolicum*) is to be looked upon as a diabolical
flower trap or as a self-protector. The insect has a pearl-
white and flattened protothorax with a sea-green edge
and, when threatened, displays the carmine coxae of its
front legs (Fig. 74*d*).

Another example is an Indian mantis (*Hymenopus
coronatus*, cf. Fig. 74*b* and 75). In its nymphal state this
insect is a mixture of pale pink and white and lives amid
pink petals. The pink abdomen is bent upward, the two
pairs of back legs have leaflike swellings, and the whole
animal has the typical opalescence of a petal.

A more appealing case of flower resemblance is found
among South American forest butterflies of the genus

FIG. 75. The larva of an African mantid (*Pseudocreo-
botra wahlbergi*) resembling the early form shown in
Figure 74*b*. (Photograph: H. R. Haefelfinger.)

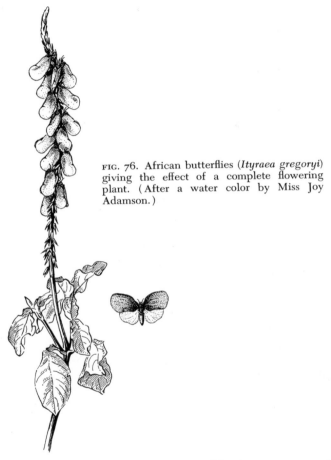

FIG. 76. African butterflies (*Ityraea gregoryi*) giving the effect of a complete flowering plant. (After a water color by Miss Joy Adamson.)

Hetaera. These butterflies have glasslike front wings and pink spots on the hind wings. As they flutter close to the ground they looked like small pink petals floating down to earth. Petal resemblance takes a peculiar form with African butterflies of the genus *Ityraea*, which settle on a stem in groups, thus producing the effect of a complete flowering plant (Fig. 76).

Resemblance to something threatening is characteristic of the larval stages of many butterflies which generally wear a concealing disguise. Some striking South American examples have been discovered. We know that hawk-moth caterpillars in their resting position may look just like twigs or dead bits of wood. However, this twig disguise has an active form when the body suddenly comes to life and twists about like a serpent (Fig. 77). Holding on to the stem with its hind legs, the caterpillar rears its body to display a dark ventral band resembling the back of a snake. The thorax and the first abdominal segment become mightily inflated and two eyespots suddenly make their appearance. The three pairs of legs in the center of the "snake's head" are pressed close to the body, and the head keeps rearing up and down until the caterpillar is reassured and returns to the resting position. The whole process of inflation and rotation involves a very high degree of behavioral organization. An African

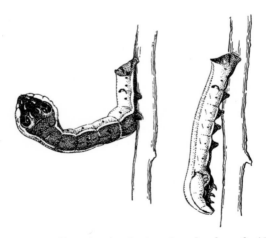

FIG. 77. A caterpillar of a South American hawk-moth (*Leucorhampha triptolemos*). Right: resting position; left: threatening position. (After Miles Moss.)

species is said to extend its pink first pair of legs, thus imitating the tongue of a snake, but reliable reports are few and far between, and many strange phenomena await more careful investigation. Much of this work can be done by amateurs, since the threatening display of large eyespots, for instance, is quite a commonplace phenomenon (Figs. 78 and 79).

Occasionally, a conspicuous part of the body may imitate a tasty titbit and so serve for trapping the prey. The last inch or so of the tails of some young pit vipers, such as the copperhead (*Agkistrodon contortrix*), are bright yellow, and they imitate worms and attract frogs and lizards by setting their tail tips writhing and twisting. Some masking crabs deliberately leave their pincers (chelae) exposed. In one (*Hyas coarctata*), for instance, the pincers are a brilliant pink and white and fishes mistake them for food. The moment a small fish comes anywhere near the otherwise camouflaged leg the trap is

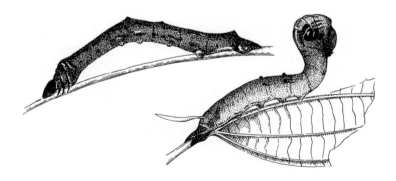

FIG. 78. The caterpillar of an American hawk-moth (*Madoryx pluto*). Left: normal position; right: threatening attitude. (After Miles Moss.)

sprung. In an aquarium one of these crabs has been observed to catch fourteen gobies in one week.

Special resemblance also diverts an enemy's attention to relatively unimportant parts of the body. It is well known that many lizards can cast off and replace their tails with ease. This power of self-mutilation enables many a marauder to feed lavishly on lizards' tails, while the tails' owners make a getaway. Some species help the process along by having very conspicuous tails. The appendage may be a radiant blue, while the rest of the body is darker and more cryptic, this difference being

FIG. 79. Sudden inflation and the appearance of eyespots in large caterpillars to strike terror. Top: caterpillar of an American hawk-moth (*Sphecodina abboti*). (After a photograph.) Bottom: caterpillar of a South American hawk-moth (*Orbya acheminedes*). (After Miles Moss.)

most striking in young lizards. During a visit to New Britain in the East Indies, H. Hediger observed that a tropical lizard (*Emoia werneri*) could be recognized by the constant flicker of its silvery tail. As he stepped into the dark jungle from the brightness outside, he was struck by the quick movement of the countless silver whips in the dark undergrowth.

A small relative of the gecko, *Psilodactylus caudicinctus,* has a tail that can be contracted so as to resemble the head. In consequence, an attacker often goes to the wrong and less important end of the body.

Turning the enemy's attention to less important parts of the body is characteristic also of a number of butterflies that simulate a false head at the wrong end of the body (Fig. 80). Here the anal angle of the hindwing is marked with an eyespot and carries a projection which looks like an antenna. As a result the insect has a new "head." Many careful investigations have shown that birds are very often taken in by these false eyes, which, together with other protective resemblances, must have great survival value.

FIG. 80. Formation of false heads in butterflies. Top: *Ialmenus evaceras;* below right: *Thecla phaleros.* The diagram at the lower left shows the adjustment of the separated parts to the pattern. (After Nicholson and Cott.)

FIG. 81. A butterfly (*Heliconius hueb-neri*) which is often mimicked sunning itself. (After photographs.)

5. *Camouflage Through Mimicry*

No form of special resemblance has attracted greater attention than the imitation of the shape, color, and behavior of offensive or disgusting animals—particularly of insects. This mimicry—like all forms of mimetic resemblance—is meant to deceive either pursuer or prey. Examples of mimicry abound in elementary textbooks, mimicry being a stock argument in favor of evolution.

Henry W. Bates, an English explorer who spent eleven years in the jungles of the Amazon, was the first to define its nature. He noticed that among batches of specimens of Heliconia butterflies (today they are subdivided into three closely related families of butterflies) there always appeared a number belonging to the Pieridae—of which the cabbage-white is an example. These intruders looked much more like Heliconias than like typical members of their own family.

Bates observed that while the Heliconias (Fig. 81) were common, conspicuously colored, and slow-flying butterflies and hence the ideal prey for many birds, the birds usually left them alone. Bates was the first to suspect that birds were sickened by some of their secretions, and this interpretation was later confirmed. Clearly, then, any resemblance to such unpalatable insects has a great survival value.

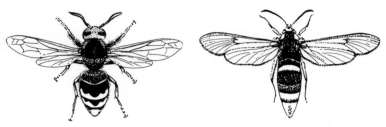

FIG. 82. Wasps as models. Left: a real wasp; right: a hornet clear-wing.

In 1864, Alfred Wallace who had anticipated Darwin's ideas on the *Origin of Species,* published further ex-amples of mimicry. After many years of observation in Malaya, he too had found that the model insects were usually common, conspicuous, slow-flying butterflies and that it was reasonable to suppose that their disagreeable taste protected them from attack.

Batesian mimicry is now the term which refers ex-clusively to the imitation of offensive properties. In Batesian mimicry an animal is not avoided instinctively; each pursuer has to learn for himself how distasteful or unpleasant the model is.

As early as 1867, Wallace expressed the opinion that many conspicuous colors were a kind of warning. Once a brightly colored insect has repelled a bird through its repulsive taste, the bird learns to associate the insect's gaudy cloak with the feeling of revulsion or pain and gives it a wide berth.

A very good example is the hornet clearwing (Fig. 82), a day-flying moth which looks like a wasp. Birds and other insect eaters, having learned by experience to avoid wasps and other stinging insects, usually treat this harmless insect in the same way.

The German naturalist Fritz Müller put forward a new point of view. Müller, who was forced to leave Germany for political reasons, settled in Brazil where he became an excellent observer of nature. He pointed out that since the insect-eating animals have to learn by experience what prey to avoid, many "protected" insects had to be sacrificed to provide the predators with experience. This form of "teaching" leads to the collective protection of a large group of insects that resemble one another in appearance, for example, all the countless insects that have the characteristic black and yellow pattern of wasps (Fig. 83). This type of mimicry is called Müllerian, to distinguish it from Batesian mimicry. Sir Edward Poulton put it this way: "Batesian mimicry is like the action of a struggling unscrupulous firm which imitates the trademark of a successful house. Müllerian mimicry is like the action of a group of powerful firms which become still better known, at a lessened cost, by combined advertisement." The *Euchelia jacobaea* caterpillar, which lives on staggerwort (*Senecio jacobaea*), is a good example of the effects of Müllerian mimicry (Fig. 84). This conspicuous black and yellow caterpillar is rejected by insect-eating birds after but the slightest acquaintance. It owes its relative safety to an odious skin secretion. Wasps, too, have a nauseating taste—due less to their skin than to their digestive organs. In consequence, birds reject all black and yellow insects after having tasted a small number of either *Euchelia* caterpillars or wasps. The more striking the pattern, the greater is the association of ideas in the birds' memory, and the smaller the number of victims. Warblers usually leave well enough alone after eight to fourteen attempts.

Euchelia caterpillars are protected in yet another way: they resemble the yellow flowers of the staggerwort among which they live. The conspicuous pattern has thus become a disguise, and while some of the caterpillars escape being eaten because of their warning coloration, others are saved by the concealing effect of the pattern.

Not many years after the discovery of mimicry, Roland Trimen was able to show how widespread it was among

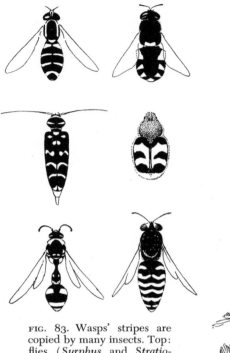

FIG. 83. Wasps' stripes are copied by many insects. Top: flies (*Syrphus* and *Stratiomys*); center: beetles (*Plagionotus* and *Trichius*); bottom: sand wasps (*Eumenes* and *Bembex*).

FIG. 84. A caterpillar (of *Euchelia jacobaea*) avoided by birds because they associate its conspicuous color with harmful insects.

African butterflies. While confirming the findings of Bates and Wallace, he added that many insects were protected by their very tough wing veins.

Mimicry has been discussed and described so often that we need not go into details, particularly since we are concerned with a subject of which mimicry is but one part. Nevertheless, we must devote a little attention to the extraordinary imitation of ants by other insects. So far the resemblance between the mimic and its model has been due to inherited patterns. The *Euchelia* caterpillar was born with its black and yellow coat, but the imitation of ants may involve changes in behavior as well. The way in which many insects imitate the characteristic triple segmentation of the narrow-waisted and wingless ant is fascinating in itself (Fig. 85). The young larva of an African grasshopper (*Myrmecophana phallax*), for instance, which lives among ants during its earliest stages, looks narrow-waisted because of three pairs of bright patches on its back that seem to be chiseled out of its broad anterior abdominal segments (Fig. 85*c*). Similar effects can be seen in a beetle (*Myrmecomaea*), whose

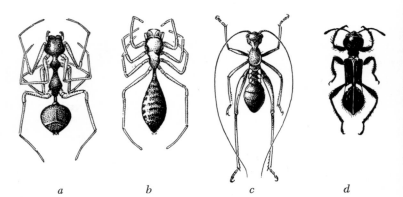

a   b   c   d

FIG. 85. The ant as a model. From left to right: spiders (*Myrmecium, Myrmarachne*), larva of a grasshopper (*Myrmecophana*), a beetle (*Myrmecomaea*).

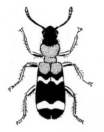 

FIG. 86. Striking likeness between a
clerid beetle and a female wasp (*Mutilla*).

two diagonal stripes imitate a waist (Fig. 85*d*). Many
other beetles, bugs, and crickets use ants as their models,
but the most astonishing ant imitations are those of spiders. Thus, one spider (*Myrmarachne*, Fig. 85*b*) walks
on only three pairs of legs while the first pair is held close
to the head, where it plays the part of an ant's antennae
by keeping the tips continually in motion.

We must also mention the strange shape of a family of
wasps. Here the wingless females are often mistaken for
ants. They have a powerful sting and are therefore excellent protective models (Fig. 86). They are imitated
by some clerid beetles and by some Ceylonese spiders
which look so much like the stinging insects that even
the male of the species (*Mutilla*) is taken in. According
to reliable reports, males have been caught while they
were trying unsuccessfully to copulate with the impersonators of their mates.

We speak of mimicry only in cases where the mimic
is protected by means of a special resemblance to a
model. Mere resemblance is not mimicry and may result
from living in the same conditions. Likeness of this kind
is called the "convergence of form," and can produce the
strangest similarities, the meaning of which we know
very little about. An example is the strange transforma-

tion of tropical celyphid flies, whose metathorax has been ballooned into a large air space that completely covers the wings and makes the fly look like a beetle (Fig. 87). Mimicry proper is just a part of these "convergent forms" and patterns.

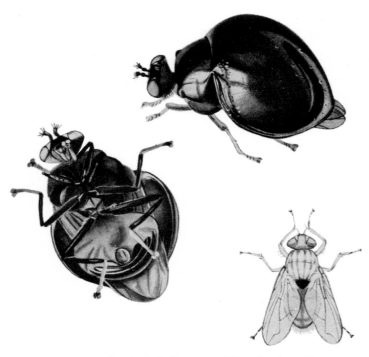

FIG. 87. Tropical celyphid flies resembling beetles. The metathorax (black triangle on lower right diagram) has been inflated into a large air space.

III. CONCEALING COLORING

1. *Colors*

White sunlight is made up of differently colored rays and, as Newton was the first to show, the color of a body is due to the rays by which it is seen and not to the body itself.

Chemical Colors

When white light falls on a body, some of the rays are absorbed while others are reflected. This is caused by the presence of substances—pigments—whose molecules pass only certain rays of the visible spectrum. Hemoglobin and chlorophyll are two typical pigments.

The dark colors of many animals are usually due to the presence of black pigment. Red, orange, and yellow are always produced by genuine pigments, but green, blue, and violet may be caused by other factors.

Structural Colors

If a body scatters *all* the light that falls on it, it will look white. Complete scattering is always the result of the random distribution of very small particles on the surface (such as the fat globules of milk or the powdered crystals of salt). The white in furs, feathers, and blossoms results from the presence of fine air bubbles between the solid tissue particles. Colors made by such molecular arrangements are called structural colors.

Also, if the particles are so small that light rays of long wave length are passed through but the short wave lengths (blue) are reflected, we find this peculiar color situation. When seen against the light, the structure appears yellow or red, but when we look at it as the light falls on it, we see it as blue. The intensity of the blue depends on the darkness of the background. The blue of the daytime sky and the red of the sunset are examples of this, as are many of the brilliant blues of insects and birds. Yellow pigment combined with structural blue produces green. This is the basis of the intense greens of so many birds. On the other hand, red pigment together with structural blue gives violet.

The pigments of animals are organic compounds that can be produced in different ways. They may be in the animal's covering—the chitin of insects and spiders, the horny hair cells of mammals, or the feathers of birds— thus preserving the color long after the animal's death. (Our natural-history museums would be rather dull places if the animals preserved had all lost their colors.) On the other hand, colors may be introduced into living cells and be as perishable as the cells themselves. Special color cells, called chromatophores, play an important part in animal color changes.

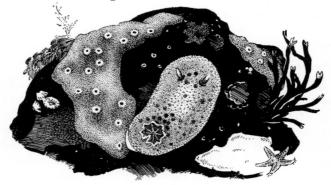

FIG. 88. Many sea lemons (*Doris*) look like the sponges on which they feed (homochromy).

2. *Color Resemblance and Environment*

While color alone may be camouflage enough, we must remember that all animals living in meadows or forests are not green, that all desert animals are not sandy-colored, and that all Arctic animals are not white.

Many animals have chromatic structures that prevent them from having certain color adaptations. Thus, mammals never have green coats. (The mature South and Central American two-toed sloth overcomes this handicap by allowing green algae to take root in its fur.)

Camouflage may be due to the color of food, and certain slugs look like the sponges or algae that they feed on (Fig. 88). In this case the pigment of the sponge seems to enter the outer layers of the skin unchanged. Transparent animals such as marine flatworms are often the color of the food in their intestines. But usually adaptive colors arise through mutation. American biologists have found that different varieties of ground squirrels and kangaroo rats live on soils that match them in color. American deer mice (*Peromyscus*) blend very well in color with the soil they live on in New Mexico. Also, a pale race of Mesopotamian desert larks (*Ammomanes deserti*) inhabits the sandy plains, while an almost black race lives on the relatively dark rocky ranges.

We must mention one more example, because it has played an important part in military camouflage. The Antarctic petrel (*Pachyptila desolata*) glides across the water with outspread wings, its color indistinguishable from that of the Antarctic Ocean. During camouflage experiments in the course of World War I, the U.S. Navy investigated the concealing properties of bluish gray colors and found that the most effective—viz. Omega gray—had the same optical properties (wave length, absorption, reflection, etc.) as did the color of the petrel's back.

3. Adaptive Color Changes

The color resemblance between an animal and its environment is called homochromy, and the proper study of camouflage involves the study of the special activities, complicated behavior patterns, and strange structures associated with homochromy..

Seasonal Color Changes

Most seasonal color changes are due to molting and subsequent replacement of hair or feathers by others of a new pattern, though white winter pelage or plumage may result from increasing the air spaces in the existing structures.

Even so, the process varies from place to place and from race to race. For instance the Ellesmere Island strain of the northern Polar hare (*Lepus arcticus*) is white all the year round, while the Hudson Bay race changes its coat between June and August. The European mountain hare (*Lepus timidus*) changes color in northern Scandinavia and in the Scottish Highlands, but in Ireland, southern Sweden, and the Faroe Islands it retains its brown coat throughout the year.

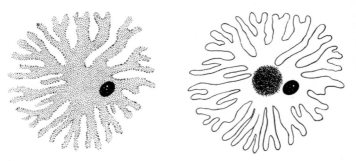

FIG. 89. The chromatophore of a fish. Expanded pigment shown on left, concentrated pigment on right. The nucleus is shaded black.

These changes in color are clearly caused by changes in the environment. Russian experiments with Siberian hares (*Lepus timidus sibiricorum*) have shown the part played by the length of day. In November, a group of ten hares, which had just changed into their winter coats, were exposed to different amounts of light. While the control animals began to change their coat to brown about the end of March, a batch that had been kept in utter darkness was still wearing its winter coat on the first of June. A third batch that had been exposed to gradually increasing light began to change fur color as early as January. The ermine's color change also has been shown to depend on the number of hours of daylight.

Some color changes are due to hereditary factors. A special strain of the Arctic fox (*Alopex lagopus*), which has a very valuable fur, keeps its blue-gray fur throughout the year, even in the deepest snow. The blue strain is dominant, and it persists even when the animals are cross-bred. Such foxes are less fertile, but even so the blue strain accounts for roughly 50 per cent of the total fox population of certain regions of East Greenland.

Rapid Color Changes

The quick color changes of fishes, amphibians, lizards, cuttlefish, squids, shrimps, and other crustaceans are due to special cells, the chromatophores, which work either independently or in an organization of chromatosomes. All except cephalopod chromatophores are alike in consisting of a branched cell with pigment in its cytoplasm (Fig. 89). The shape is constant, and the pigment either fills all the branches—then the animal is colored—or is concentrated in the center—and then the animal turns paler. Some chromatophores contain several pigments, and each of these pigments may respond to a separate stimulus. A number of pigments in one cell suggests complicated submicroscopic structures such as paths within the cells which the pigments may travel along separately.

We can see how complex these rapid color changes are by looking at the skin on the back of an American anole (*Anolis carolinensis*), often misnamed the American chameleon. A thin layer of very small droplets under the skin fills the space between larger cells with yellow pigment (Fig. 90). The droplets touch the skin and even come between its cells. In addition to intracellular pigment, this region also contains yellow pigment cells. Below them are layers of fairly large, cube-shaped cells containing very fine purine crystals. The position of these cells makes an intense structural blue, which is changed into lustrous green by the thin layer of droplets, which make a yellow filter. Below the cube-shaped cells are large black cells, the melanophores, whose branches, or rays, reach right up to the skin. When the black pigment of the melanophores is drawn back from the skin, the anole turns a light green, but when the pigment is expanded to fill the branches the color is dark green. The same kind of color changes take place in the common frog.

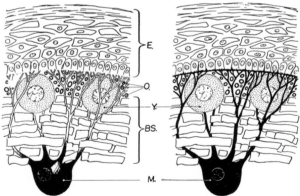

FIG. 90. Chromatophores in the skin of the American anole (*Anolis carolinensis*). Right: expanded black pigment (melanin). *E*, epidermis; *O*, layer of droplets acting as yellow filter; *Y*, yellow pigment cells; *BS*, layer of structural blue; *M*, melanophores.

Though most chromatophores are similar in structure, they are made active in entirely different ways.

The most important organ in bringing about color changes is the eye. If we lay a plaice against two sharply divided colors, its whole body turns the color of that section of the field that the eye happens to see. Yet the visual sense is not the only one to excite the chromatophores. For instance, frogs change color depending on whether they are placed on a rough or smooth support, and *Hyperia,* an amphipod crustacean which is quite transparent and indistinguishable from the jellyfish on which it lives, turns a muddy brown the moment it is taken off the jellyfish and left to swim about freely. Apparently, these color changes are brought about by stimulation of the sense of feeling.

Stimulation reaches the chromatophores of different animals in different ways. These special cells may be controlled either by directly stimulating the nerves or by hormones—substances carried directly into the blood stream by special glands.

The most marvelous color responses are those of cephalopods, such as the squid. Their chromatophores differ considerably in color. Each color organ is a central rounded body bounded by an elastic membrane and contains finely divided pigment and a nucleus. Attached to the outside membrane is a system of long raylike muscle fibers, and the other ends of these fibers are branched and reach into the central tissue. Each fiber has a nucleus at the outer end. When the system is at rest the membrane squeezes all the fluid to the center and the chromatophore is invisible, but when the muscles contract the spherical cell is pulled into the shape of an expanded disk, and the pigment spreads out (Fig. 91). The whole process is controlled by color centers in the brain, and these can be overruled by a general color center, probably in the central ganglia. The color changes are emphasized by cells containing iridescent material

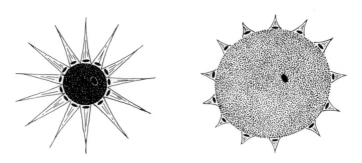

FIG. 91. Cephalopod chromatophores. Left: radial muscles relaxed, right: muscles contracted with the membrane stretched.

which can reflect light and produce white or pearly-white patterns.

Squids have a highly developed color sense, and while they change color to camouflage themselves, the main reason is to make known their personal states—for example, sexual excitement.

Rapid color changes in crustaceans.   The transparency of many crustaceans has helped us to study their chromatic structures and to understand better the part that hormones play in making the chromatophores active. While some amphipods (sand fleas) and isopods (wood lice) change color strikingly, the higher crustaceans (decapods, Fig. 92) change much more and in them a single chromatophore can contain four different pigments, each answering to a separate stimulus.

The chromatophores of crustaceans react to visual responses and to direct exposure to light. Color changes in response to stimuli received by the upper half of the compound eye are different from those due to stimuli received by the lower half: while the former causes the

FIG. 92. A shrimp (*Leander serratus*), whose color changes have been carefully investigated.

black pigment alone to expand, the latter causes all the pigments to spread out.

However, even apart from eyes and eyestalks, light can have a direct effect on crustacean chromatophores. Visual stimuli affect these chromatophores because crustacean chromatophores are not directly controlled by the nervous system, but are made active by hormones.

G. Koller showed that the eyestalk produces a substance which causes dark pigment to contract. This finding led to a careful examination of the eyestalk (Fig. 93) and to the discovery of the sinus gland and the X organ.

These organs are connected with color changes. At first the sinus "gland" was believed to be a hormone-producing gland, but now it is considered a hormone-collecting center regulating the flow of hormones into the blood stream. Different crustacean hormones make different pigments active.

While eyestalk extracts whiten shrimps, they darken the fiddler crab (*Uca*) that lives in the sand or mud of temperate waters (Fig. 94). The removal of the eyestalk darkens shrimps and blanches the fiddler crab. But strangely enough, the hormones of both eyestalks are identical—the extract from the fiddler crab eyestalks has a "normal" blanching effect on shrimps. The difference must be due to unknown factors in the chromatophores themselves. Another difference is that while the shrimps change color to adapt themselves, the fiddler crab shows anger, fear, sexual excitement, and so on by changing color.

We conclude this section with a brief discussion of a small prawn (*Hippolyte*) that lives amid coastal algae and seaweed. Like most of its relatives, the prawn is transparent and spends its earliest youth on the high seas.

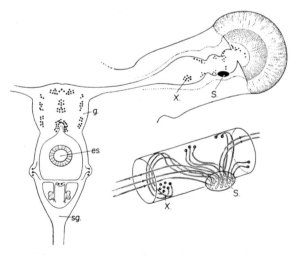

FIG. 93. The brain and eyestalk of a shrimp. The dots indicate the hormone-producing cells. The lower-right diagram shows the hormones being collected in the sinus gland, in which the cells end. g, supraesophageal ganglion; es, esophagus; sg, subesophageal ganglion; S, sinus gland; X, X organ. (After various authors.)

FIG. 94. The fiddler crab (*Uca*) changes color to show anger, fear, etc. (After Crane.)

Later, it migrates toward the coastal zone. This prawn has been studied for more than fifty years, and its color rhythm has been clearly established. At night all the pigments contract and the animal turns a transparent blue, but in the daytime it becomes a master of camouflage, turning green when among seaweed, violet among coralline algae, and brown, red, or orange, as the need arises. But the most surprising color effects are displayed when the prawn settles on leaves covered by a growth of opaque coralline algae (*Melobesia*) with colors ranging from pink to violet (Fig. 95). The prawn imitates the spots of algae to perfection, even forming opaque stripes that increase the deceptive effect.

Young prawns (*Hippolyte*)—up to 20mm in size—can completely change within ten minutes, older stages need between twenty-four and forty-eight hours, and mature specimens must first molt to alter their appearance. For this reason the oldest animals move elsewhere rather than change their color.

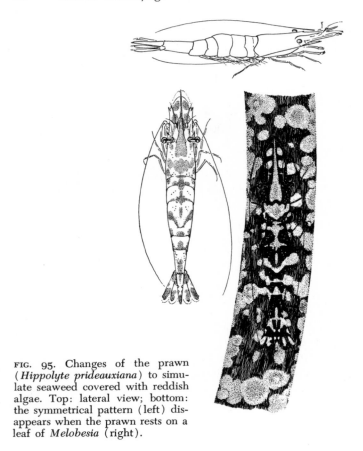

FIG. 95. Changes of the prawn (*Hippolyte prideauxiana*) to simulate seaweed covered with reddish algae. Top: lateral view; bottom: the symmetrical pattern (left) disappears when the prawn rests on a leaf of *Melobesia* (right).

Rapid color changes in fish. Whenever we speak about color changes we immediately think of the chameleon, an animal that has fascinated mankind ever since Aristotle first described it. This has made us forget that the greatest masters of disguise by far are fishes. The cells by which they change color are black, red, yellow, white, and iridescent chromatophores, which are connected to the nerve centers by means of nerve fibers. The expansion and contraction of pigment are thus under the rapid control of the nervous system. Color changes to fit the background are set off by the eyes and to a lesser extent by special light perceptors in the skin. While the nervous system normally sends these stimuli straight to the chromatophores, sometimes it also stimulates the pituitary gland to deliver its hormones to the blood stream. When hormones reach the chromatophores, the black pigment expands. Nervous stimuli along the sympathetic system have the opposite effect.

Fishes change their color for other purposes than adapting themselves to their background. They may show sexual excitement, aggression, submission, and so on by changing color. Clearly, chromatophore responses in fish are very complex.

Flounder and related flatfish (Fig. 96) show the most remarkable color changes. In early life, after a brief period of normal symmetry, their eyes and mouth travel to the colored side of the body, while the inconspicuous side lies flat on the ground. The flounder change color to an unusually high degree to fit the background, and the chromatophores respond not only by color changes but by changes in pattern.

Rapid color changes in amphibians and reptiles. The changes in color that amphibians make to agree with their background are largely due to melanophore responses together with movements of yellow or orange pigments, the white cells containing immobile crystals. The permanent markings of the frog contain movable pigments and can darken or lighten. The darkening seems due to the disappearance of a pituitary hormone from the blood stream, but it may also come from a blanching hormone or direct nervous stimulation. While the latter has recently been demonstrated, it is not of much influence, as color changes as slow as those of amphibians are always due to hormones.

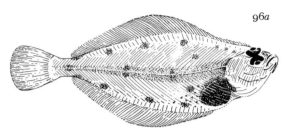

96a

FIG. 96. Color changes in the flatfish. (*a*) Young flounder with typical color arrangement. (*b–d*) *Platophrys podas* changes its color for different backgrounds. (Photograph: British Museum.)

The influence of the environment on color changes has been studied particularly in the case of frogs. While the chief stimuli are visual, the frog's skin also sets off color changes in response to cold, warmth, touch, and moisture differences.

Because of this great variety of responses the frog and the toad appear in a host of disguises. Miss Stephenson tells of a lady gardener who was convinced that her small ornamental garden contained three toads: a spotted brown one among the rocks, a light green one in the rhododendron bushes, and an olive-colored one at the bottom of a little pool. It took the lady a long time to realize that her garden had but a single toad!

The chromatic structure of reptiles differs from species to species. Our knowledge is largely based on three lizards (Fig. 97), the best known being the anole (*Anolis*) —the "American chameleon." This greenish-brown lizard has a very simple chromatophore-activation system. The chromatophores are controlled by pituitary hormones, which cause darkening. The anole changes color to show anger, fear, and so on, and the effect of disguise appears to be only of slight importance.

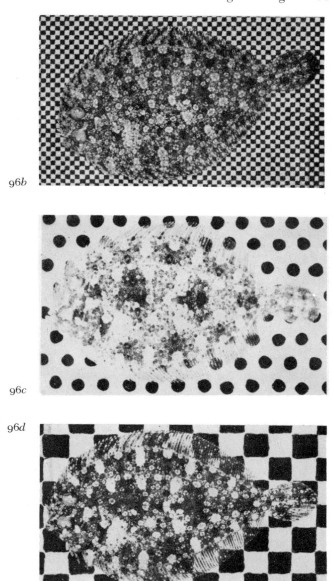

96b

96c

96d

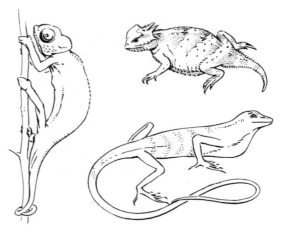

FIG. 97. Left: African chameleon; top right: ground lizard (*Phrynosoma*); bottom right: the American anole (*Anolis*).

The ground lizard (*Phrynosoma*) of western America has a more complicated chromatic organization. The pituitary hormone causes darkening, but another substance causes lightening.

As might be expected, the chameleon has the most complicated chromatophore system of all. In fact, this system is so involved that its meaning is not at all definite. The chameleon has three layers of pigment: yellow, black, and red. Deep layers of guanophores act as reflectors, and the structural blue of their upper zone combines with the yellow pigment to make green. Camouflage is largely controlled by movements of black pigment, and the other color changes show states such as fear. Light and temperature are also important, for the skin that is exposed to direct light turns darker than the surrounding area.

Watching a pet chameleon has revealed that color changes showing fear may have a threatening effect. Whenever the dog ran after this chameleon, the chameleon turned in its tracks, opened its pink mouth, and changed to a dark color. Its threatening attitude and darkening always caused the dog to retreat.

The chameleon's chromatophores respond to stimuli both to the skin and to vision. Investigators do not agree as to whether a stimulus to the skin makes the melanophores active directly or by way of the central nervous system, but it is known that nerve excitation has a whitening effect. The disagreement is even wider on the question of hormone activation. In any case the chameleon is not only a master of camouflage, but its every mood is reflected by different colors—a language of colors that is most difficult to interpret.

Color Changes in Insects

Color changes in insects are not as striking as we might expect them to be, for while their horny shells contain pigments or produce structural colors, these colors are usually permanent. Life in water is far more favorable to spontaneous color changes.

For a start, insects generally lack chromatophores. The aquatic larva of the *Corethra* mosquito has melanophores on its swim bladders, but they serve for heat and gaseous exchanges rather than chromatic responses.

Color changes happen in isolated cases, for instance in dragonflies (Fig. 98). Here, long exposure to the new environment and molting are necessary before the color can be changed. The color changes are due to melanin which forms in the skin cells and then enters the top layer of the newly formed shell. The new color appears before the old shell is cast off.

Other insects resemble the dragonfly in this respect. We know that the color of a small water bug (*Sigora*) is determined by the color of its environment *before* its last molting. Also, in the wingless stages of the locust's life similar color changes, involving black and yellow pigment, take place.

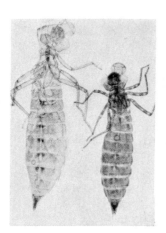

FIG. 98. Dragonflies. Left: change to suit a light background. Right: change to fit a dark background. In each case the smaller larva was exposed to the new background for some time before turning the color of the larger larva. (After F. Krieger.)

In this connection we may also mention the pupa of the cabbage butterfly (*Pieris brassicae*). The color differences of this pupa are the result of different proportions of white epidermal pigment and black pigment in the outermost layer of the horny armor.

Another example of color changes is the Middle Eastern grasshopper (*Acrida turrita*), which may look yellow, green, red, gray, or violet. Changes in color involve molting and take a long time. This grasshopper lacks melanophores and uses other pigments instead. Many kinds of grasshopper show similar color responses.

The brown strain of the notorious phasmid grasshopper (*Carausius morosus*) grows paler or darker in response to a great number of stimuli. Recently, these color changes (which are hormone-activated) have attracted the attention of many investigators, but the problem has so far not been completely solved. The hormones are produced by a brain center and the animals have a daily rhythm, turning brighter in the day and darker at night. Light, temperature, heat, and humidity all produce responses in this grasshopper. The actual color change is due to contraction or spreading of pigment in the hypodermal cells.

IV. THE SIGNIFICANCE
OF CAMOUFLAGE

Protective and warning colors—resemblance to leaf, branch, or bark, or imitation of offensive animals—interest the scientist because of the important part they have played in the evolution of species.

Darwin proposed the idea that very small variations took place in different generations of one species. In the last fifty years we have learned that such variations may be hereditary and that hereditary variations (mutations) are biologically neutral—they neither aid nor impede survival, any variety being eliminated by natural enemies or unfavorable factors or preserved by friendlier conditions.

The many camouflages we have mentioned were said to be the result of the selection of favorable mutations during thousands of years. If disguises look as if they have been just "made for the eyes," it is because all of this time the marauders' eyes have been doing all the selecting.

To prove these assumptions, it had to be shown that a protectively colored kind of animal would survive where another would not, and also that animal hunters avoid conspicuously colored stinging insects and their imitators. Darwinism—or rather neo-Darwinism—stands and falls by the results.

1. The Effects of Protective Coloring

Color adaptation itself needs no proof, but its survival value does. We have pointed out the importance of the eye as a "selector," and birds with their keen sight are ideal for experiment—particularly as their weak sense of smell cannot affect the results.

Experiments have shown important results. Professor F. B. Sumner used as bait small "mosquito fish" (*Gambusia patruelis*), well known for the part they have played in getting rid of malarial mosquito larvae. The fish were kept in two large tanks. The inside of one tank was black and the other was white. After several weeks, the fish had changed color—to a darker shade in the black tank, to a lighter shade in the white tank. Then an equal number of dark and light fish were placed in an experimental tank, either black, in which case the light fish were more conspicuous, or light gray, where the dark fish were more conspicuous. Galapagos penguins (*Spheniscus mendiculus*) were then allowed to try to catch them.

In the combined experiments 1150 out of 2672 fish were caught by the penguins. 395 (34 per cent) of the fish caught were of the color-adapted shade and 755 (66 per cent) were of the nonadapted shade. This experiment clearly proved the relative survival value of color adaptation.

A great deal of interest was aroused by Lee R. Dice's experiments with owls and deer mice (*Peromyscus maniculatus*). These experiments not only led to a better understanding of the general problem of camouflage but showed the protective value of color adaptation even at dusk or at night. Dice used four different-colored kinds of deer mice against different-colored background fields. Each field was divided into two compartments, roughly nine feet by ten feet. Knowing that owls can find their prey by sound alone on open ground, he turned the floor into an artificial forest: twelve-inch sticks were used to divide the fields into eight-inch squares. The sticks were joined to one another four inches from the ground, and the whole field was dimly illuminated. Different varieties of deer mice were offered to the owl for fifteen minutes at a time, and each field had four pale and four dark mice. In thirteen experiments thirty-three pale and fifty-eight dark mice were caught on a light background, and sixty-seven pale and thirty-eight dark ones were caught on a dark background. Combining the results, 125 nonadapted and only seventy-one adapted rodents were caught. Dice's experiments give further evidence for the survival value of color adaptation.

John H. Gerould once found a blue mutation of the caterpillar of the clouded-yellow butterfly (*Colias philodice*). The normal green strain is inconspicuous in the clover it feeds on. Gerould exposed a mixed collection of the caterpillars—with one-third to one-quarter of them blue mutants—to the attack of sparrows. After ten days the survivors were all green ones except for two very small and undeveloped blue caterpillars. Almost all of the blue ones had been eaten.

Another striking experiment was recently carried out in Turkey (Fig. 99). Grasshopper larvae (*Oedipoda* and *Acrida*) were exposed to the keen eyes of an ibis-like bird (*Geronticus eremita*) on light and dark squares as on a chessboard. Brownish or grayish larvae (*Oedipoda*) were placed on the squares, which were covered respec-

FIG. 99. Chessboard experiment using *Geronticus* and grasshoppers. (After Ergene.)

tively by brown and gray pebbles taken from the habitat of the larvae. (The larvae were used because they lack the conspicuous bright color of the adults' hindwings.) In the experiments with the green or yellow grasshopper larvae (*Acrida*) the chessboard was covered with corn-seed and straw, respectively. The animals were tied to threads so they could move about.

In these experiments sixteen larvae at a time were exposed, and the bird was let loose on them for two minutes. The chessboard field was rearranged with every experiment, so the bird could not learn to pick certain squares.

As a result in fifty-seven experiments with *Oedipoda*, out of 251 larvae the bird caught, 236 were nonadapted and only 15 were adapted. In 91 experiments with *Acrida*, the bird caught 617 larvae, 559 nonadapted and only 58 adapted.

These and many similar experiments clearly show the positive selection effect of color adaptation.

2. The Effects of Warning Coloring

The vertebrate animals—such as birds, mammals, and fish—do not avoid stinging and other injurious insects instinctively, and each new generation must learn which unpleasant sensations are associated with what conspicuous colors. Even though a few insect eaters prefer bold insects such as wasps, most of them quickly learn to give such insects a wide berth. Investigators have tried to discover what effect this has on the survival of conspicuous insects.

I. H. N. Kluijver collected food samples by placing neck collars (worn for short periods) on starling nestlings, thus preventing the young birds from swallowing the food brought to them by their parents. In this way he gathered 17,933 food animals, including 16,484 insects. Among them were 4490 beetles and weevils (Coleoptera), with only two disagreeable-tasting ladybugs and 799 Hymenoptera with not a single bee or wasp except one fossorial wasp (*Crabro cribrarius*).

G. D. Hale Carpenter found that of 157 insects captured by feeding monkeys 113 were inconspicuous and only 44 had warning colors. Of 218 thrown away, 176 had warning colors and 42 were inconspicuous. In other words, of 220 animals with warning colors 176 were refused, and only 42 out of 155 with dull colors. Clearly, warning colors have a great selective effect.

Experiments with jays to discover how much protection is given geometrid moth caterpillars by their rigid attitude and concealing colors show that the birds do not usually see the caterpillars, but occasional jays may find them and afterward mistake most twigs for caterpillars. Such frustration teaches the birds to avoid *all* twigs, caterpillars included!

After trying a few times to eat wasps, birds avoid them. Wasps, bees, and *Euchelia* caterpillars disgust and sicken birds. An uncolored mash consisting of the organs of these insects is always rejected by them. The experiments, while they show that birds can learn, also show that they forget what they have learned in about three months. Even so, wasps and their imitators are protected four times out of five.

3. The Role of Vision

Camouflage is *optical* deception. Our survey would therefore be incomplete without examining briefly the part the eye plays in selecting things.

Only animals with a highly developed convex eye may be considered as selectors. Thus, most spiders which catch their prey by the sense of touch and all animals that hunt by smell must be ignored. In fact our observations are restricted to vertebrates, since the role of the compound eye has not yet been sufficiently investigated.

In the last ten years many higher animals have been found to have a color sense like our own. While the details are still uncertain (infrared radiation and the vision of owls, the function of color filters in the eyes of birds), we know that the outer part of the optical system of most vertebrates is like ours.

Likeness of eyes is not in itself evidence for likeness of seeing, since the central nervous system decides what is really "seen"—the details that are picked out and noticed. The organization of the central nervous system is far more complex than that of the eye, but even so, behaviorists have been able to throw a great deal of light on just this problem within the last twenty years. Although psychologists have rightly stressed how difficult it is to take a bird's-eye view of things, comparative psychology has shown that the laws of vision which produce optical illusions in man are likely to operate in other vertebrates as well.

CONCLUSION

The remote and the strange always have a special appeal to our minds. When we think about camouflage in the animal world, we are apt to picture the famous *Kallima* butterfly of India, which copies the pattern of a dead leaf with fantastic exactness. But we do not need to go to India for examples of camouflage; we can find plenty of beautiful ones in our own back yards. In Europe, for instance, the common orange-tip butterfly illustrates a whole series of camouflage principles.

By way of review we can consider the appearance of the orange-tip butterfly (*Euchloë cardamines*).

We first meet this butterfly among the early blossoms of the cuckooflower—the male, with its orange and white wings, being a welcome harbinger of spring.

Let us first examine the caterpillar. With its hairy green coat, its sprinkling of fine black dots, and its white, lengthwise stripes it looks like the cruciferous plant on which the egg was laid. Its markings are characteristic of many pierid caterpillars and are an inherited variation. Now a particular variation is optically neutral—it is indifferently protective or conspicuous. In European pierids the effect is usually concealing, the lengthwise stripes dividing the narrow body into two green streaks which look inconspicuous among the stems and leaves of the cuckooflower.

The pupa suspends itself in a sling, resembling the flower's maturing pods. The very slim and tapering pupa (Fig. 100) doubles up backward until most of the light falls on its underside, the wing cases bulging out in the opposite direction. A lateral edge helps to give the two-surface counter-shading typical of the clouded-yellow butterfly (*Colias edusa*). A closer look reveals that although the original pupa was green, it has now changed into a yellow-brown that blends well with the dry leaves and stalks of its winter quarters. This masterful disguise is particularly important for our orange tip, since its pupal stage lasts into the spring.

The butterfly (imago), when it finally emerges, also displays a wealth of colorful tricks. In flight, or while sunning itself, the male is a brilliant white and orange, its color emphasized by a dark-brown tip (Fig. 101). The hindwings seem dappled with grayish green, for the green markings of the underside show through. (The female is without the orange patch, and resembles the cabbage-white, to which she is related.) Now, the male's conspicuousness is no quirk of nature—its markings are characteristic of all the Pieridae, a world-wide family of butterflies. To judge the effects of selection on the origin of the orange-tips' color and pattern we must mark the characteristic appearance of the whole family.

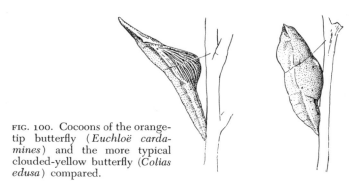

FIG. 100. Cocoons of the orange-tip butterfly (*Euchloë cardamines*) and the more typical clouded-yellow butterfly (*Colias edusa*) compared.

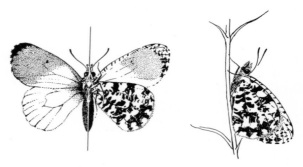

FIG. 101. Orange-tip butterfly (*Euchloë cardamines*). Left: combined upper side and underside; right: resting position.

The moment the colorful pierid butterfly comes to rest, it is quite unrecognizable. It folds its wings over its back, and the bright patches of color suddenly disappear. This resting position itself is not necessarily protective, for it is typical of all butterflies no matter how conspicuous the underside of their wings. All of them are invisible when seen straight from the top, but a side view immediately betrays the more conspicuous ones. The orange-tip, however, is not to be caught in this way. Its underside has green markings and these afford him perfect camouflage against the right background. Actually, the green markings are not really green, but are a mixture of dark-brown scales and occasional yellow scales. The total effect is heightened by the upper wing, which has a mottled pattern exactly where it shows through in the resting position.

The wings look as if they had been sprayed while joined together, for the orange-tip is an example of pattern joining. The joining effect is particularly clear, as the orange part of the underside of the forewing is completely hidden when the hindwing is closed.

This small butterfly therefore combines a wealth of visual effects—some concealing, others revealing.

The secret of visual effects (a colorful flower, the wing of a butterfly, the markings of a fish) is no less mysterious than sight itself, and biologists divide their attention between them. This little book was meant as an introduction to the work that is being done in this field.

But over and above this, I sincerely hope the reader will observe his surroundings more closely to find greater joy and pleasure in the simple contemplation of nature. A very short description of the life of the orange-tip butterfly has shown how fascinating such observations can be. In making his own contribution to man's store of scientific knowledge, the reader may well find his own life greatly enriched.

INDEX

Now available

Ann Arbor Science Library Paperbacks

AAS 501   **THE STARS** by W. Kruse and W. Dieckvoss

AAS 502   **THE ANTS** by Wilhelm Goetsch

AAS 503   **THE SENSES** by Wolfgang von Buddenbrock

AAS 504   **LIGHT: VISIBLE AND INVISIBLE** by Eduard Ruechardt

AAS 505   **THE BIRDS** by Oskar and Katharina Heinroth

AAS 506   **EBB AND FLOW: The Tides of Earth, Air, and Water** by Albert Defant

AAS 507   **ANIMAL CAMOUFLAGE** by Adolf Portmann

AAS 508   **PLANET EARTH** by Karl Stumpff

AAS 509   **VIRUS** by Wolfhard Weidel

AAS 510   **THE SUN** by Karl Kiepenheuer

and other titles to follow

The University of Michigan Press